Captain Beaky

by
Jeremy Lloyd

illustrated by
Keith Michell

CHAPPELL & COMPANY LIMITED

This book is for three children I'm very fond of . . .
Sascha, Julian and Anouska

Stories of Captain Beaky and his friends are
available on:—

An album, single and cassette from Polydor Records;
written by **Jeremy Lloyd** and set to music by **Jim Parker.**
Featuring **Jeremy Lloyd, Keith Michell, Harry Secombe,
Peter Sellers** and **Twiggy.**

The sheet music to the Captain Beaky single and
songbook are available from Chappell Music Ltd.

L.P. 2383 462
Cassette 3170 462
Single POS P106

Songbook 2138
Sheet Music 5265

First published 1976
First published in paperback 1980
© Captain Beaky Limited 1977
Illustrations © 1976
All characters depicted in the book are
the sole and exclusive property of the
Owner and shall not be reproduced in any
form without the Owner's consent.

Chappell & Company Limited
50 New Bond Street, London W1A 2BR

London Amsterdam Brussels Hamburg
Johannesburg Madrid Milan Paris
Stockholm Sydney Toronto Wellington
Zurich New York

Poems are set in 'Monophoto' Photina by
Filmtype Services Limited, Scarborough

Printed in Great Britain by
The Burlington Press (Cambridge) Ltd.,
Foxton, Cambridge CB2 6SW

ISBN 0 903443 38 4

List of Poems

Captain Beaky

The bravest animals in the land
Are Captain Beaky and his band.
That's Timid Toad, Reckless Rat,
Artful Owl and Batty Bat,
March through the woodland
Singing songs
That tell how they have righted wrongs.
Once Hissing Sid, an evil snake,
Kept the woodland folk awake
In fear and trembling every night
In case he gave someone a bite.

Said Artful Owl, 'We'll lie in wait
And one of us will be the bait.'
Said Captain Beaky, 'Have no fear
For I alone will volunteer.'

'No make it me,' said Reckless Rat,
'I'll stand there in my reckless hat
When Hissing Sid picks up my trail
I'll just lasso him with my tail.'

'Good idea,' said Timid Toad,
'We'll hide a long way down the road.
And when you've overcome resistance
We'll rush along to your assistance.'

Said Batty Bat, 'I've got a wheeze,
I'll fly and hide up in the trees.
If Hissing Sid should slither by,
I'll drop a boulder from the sky.'

Said Artful Owl, 'The idea's sound.
How will you lift it off the ground?'
Poor Batty Bat just scratched his head,
'I hadn't thought of that,' he said.

Said Owl, 'The rest of us hold back,
There's only one that he'll attack.'
Said Timid Toad, 'I like your plan.'
'Good luck,' said Owl, 'For you're the man.'

So Timid Toad, his eyes a-popping,
Into the woodland night went hopping.
Captain Beaky waved his hand
Followed with his trusted band
That's Artful Owl and Reckless Rat.
Above the trees flew Batty Bat.

'Stop,' said Beaky, 'I hear squeaking.'
'It's Batty Bat,' said Owl, 'He's speaking.'
'It's all in code,' said Reckless Rat.
Said Owl, 'I'll just decipher that.'

'A dash, a dot, two short, two long,
I rather hope I've got it wrong.
It reads, can clearly see the road.
Hissing Sid has captured Toad.'

'Quick men,' said Beaky, 'No delay,
You mustn't let him get away.'
And leaping off, said, 'Follow me,'
And ran head first into a tree.

'Dot – dot – dot,' squeaked Batty Bat.
Said Beaky, 'Quick, decipher that.'
Cried Reckless Rat, 'Perhaps we're gaining.'
'No,' said Owl, 'He says it's raining.'

Oh how they ran to save poor Toad,
For they must find that Snake's abode.
Guided by old Batty Bat,
Dot – dot, go this way,
Dash – go that.

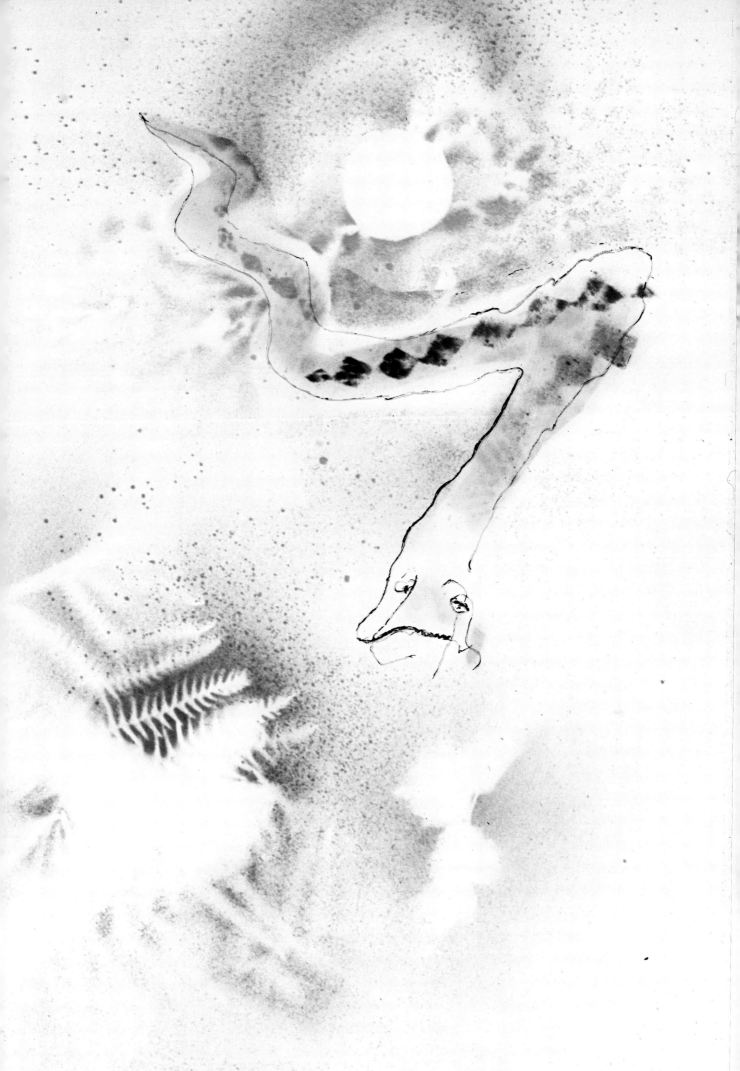

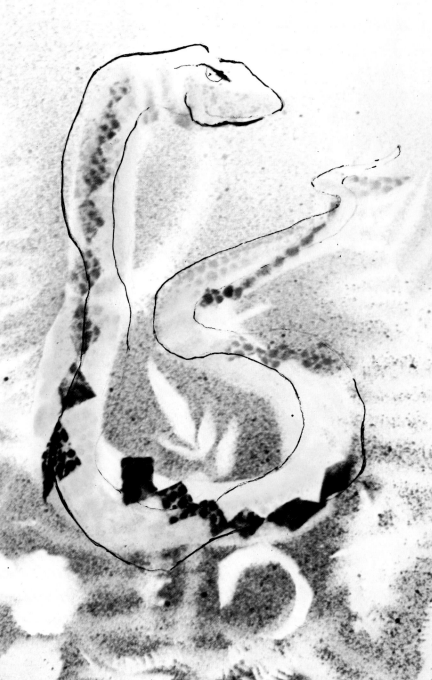

Then Hissing Sid's lair they espied.
Were they too late? Was he inside?
Said Reckless Rat, 'I'll get a pole,
And stop him going down his hole.'

Then into sight the Snake came hopping,
Right past his hole, no sign of stopping.
Said Reckless Rat, 'That's rather funny,
There's something jumping in his tummy.'

Said Captain Beaky, 'Well, I'm blowed,
Hissing Sid has swallowed Toad.'
And as the Snake hopped out of sight,
Off they chased into the night.

At last they found him, tired and dizzy
And pulled out Toad, who said, 'Where is he?
For left alone, I felt quite sick
And hopped into a hollow stick.'

Said Owl, 'A clever step to take,
You jumped into that Slippery Snake.'
'That was brave of Toad,' said Rat.
'That's just my sort of plan,' said Bat.

Said Captain Beaky to his men,
'We'll not see Hissing Sid again.'
And as they marched off down the road,
They sang in praise of Timid Toad.

Above them flew old Batty Bat,
With his wings stretched out quite flat.
Owl's idea, that clever fellah,
To have a flying umberella.

Blanche

A baby owl, whose name was Blanche,
Perched bravely on a narrow branch,
And wondered whether she should try,
To jump off and attempt to fly.
She bravely counted up to ten,
And then she counted ten again.
She jumped!
She found she couldn't fly
And lay there looking at the sky.
'It's lucky that that branch,' said she,
'Was on the ground, and not the tree.'
Then off she ran
And flapped her wings
And said 'These are most awkward things.
For though I skip and jump quite high,
I'm still no nearer to the sky.'

And falling down she gave a howl
And wished she'd never been an owl!
Till finally her mother found her,
And put a great big wing around her,
Then said, 'Dear Blanche, don't be upset,
You haven't grown your feathers yet.'

The Bumble Bee

In his brown and yellow sweater,
Buzzing round the hollyhocks,
Flys a great big bumble bee
Wearing thick black woolly socks.
For bumble bees just live for pleasure
And never work a single day,
Oh what a lovely life of leisure
Just to buzz around and play.
In a big snapdragon snoozing
When the sun is just too hot
Then round the flowerbeds busy cruising
To find another comfy spot.
But there's a problem rather puzzling
And no one's solved the mystery.
Who knits those socks and big striped sweaters?
Can't be lazy bumble bees!

Castle Doom

In the dreaded Castle Doom
In a locked up turret room,
Lived the Hairy Nairn of Nairn
Since he was a wee wee bairn.
Fed by ancient Miss MacFeeling,
Through a big hole in the ceiling.
Alas, he'd never learnt to eat!
Except for great big chunks of meat.
And when an egg appeared he'd snatch it
Then sit on it and try to hatch it.
He'd pour his porridge on his head
And eat his porridge bowl instead,
And when he got a pair of kippers
He made them into carpet slippers.
Until one Christmas, Miss MacFeeling
Put a haggis through the ceiling.
Unaccustomed to such sights
He tried to play it like the pipes.
Alas, of course, no sound emitted
And with a roar of rage he bit it,
And then, the Hairy Nairn of Nairn,
Locked up since he was a bairn,
Smiled a hairy smile and said,
'No more porridge on my head.
No more great big chunks of meat,
No more kippers on my feet,
No more eggs I'll try to hatch,
No more food I'll have to snatch.'
And with a big contented sigh,
Said, 'I'll eat the bagpipes till I die!'

Michell

Cyril the Centipede

Cyril the centipede
Loved playing games,
And his favourite one was football.
And when he played goal
With nine fleas and a mole
Nothing got past him at all.

They played spiders and newts
But his one hundred boots
Gave his team very little to do
And the fleas would get bored,
The mole never scored
And the crowd would just stand there and boo.

'Til one awful day the crowd stayed away
And no fans for either side came,
But all said and done
When it's none none none none,
It's really not much of a game.
Then Cyril the centipede
Hurt his back leg
The hundre'th one down on the right
So he used a small stick
And went 99 click,
Now I'm happy to say it's all right,
But he doesn't play goal
Any more – he's retired
Unbeaten, for nobody scored.
Now he just referees
For the spiders and fleas,
And even the mole
Has just scored.

Dennis the Dormouse

Young Dennis the dormouse
Was frightfully frail
And hated to hear a hinge squeak.
And should a door slam at the height of a gale
He'd retire to his bed for a week.

A rattly old chain
Would give him a jolt
And he'd get wobbly knees and go pale.
And even the sound of a softly drawn bolt
Made him cover his ears with his tail.

So he searched round the house
For a small can of oil
And a couple of sticks and some twine
Which he made into stilts with much labour and toil.
Now Dennis the dormouse is fine.

For he's oiled the locks
Of each room in the house,
All the bolts and the hinges as well.
And everything now is as quiet as a mouse,
What a pity he can't reach the bell.

Desmond the Duck

With foxes abroad
Few ducks can afford
To leave a new egg in a nest,
And should they do so
They usually go
For it's duck eggs that foxes like best.
And Desmond the duck
Had awfully bad luck,
Even before he was born,
Whilst still in his egg
With his nose round his leg
A fox came and took him at dawn.
Unaware of his plight
And the subsequent flight
Of the fox with the egg he had snatched,
Desmond tapped on his shell
And let out a yell
For he thought it was time he was hatched.
The fox stopped with surprise,
And in front of his eyes
A small beak appeared through a crack,
Then a head, then a leg
Appeared from the egg
Then Desmond, who fell on his back.
'Look Mummy,' he said,
'There's a bump on my head,
But I couldn't wait there any longer,
And now I've been born,
Will you please keep me warm,
And take care of me till I grow stronger.'
The fox shook his head,
'I'm sorry,' he said,
'But alas there's no going back.
I'm a fox, you're a duck,
That's right out of luck,
And I'm taking you home for a snack.'
Said Desmond, 'All right,
I could do with a bite,
But first could you answer my question.
What are these on my back?
And why can't you quack?'
Said the fox, 'You've upset my digestion.

I'll take you back home,
My heart isn't stone,
And life as a duck can be fun.
On the rivers and lakes
You can play ducks and drakes,
Quite often I've wished I was one.'
Said Desmond, 'Hooray,
What fun, come and play
Any time that you're passing and bored.'
Said the fox with a smile,
'It'll be a long while,
For foxes are always abroad.'

Michael

Eloise the Silkworm

There was a lady silkworm,
Whose name was Eloise,
Whose sister Sybil Silkworm,
Was very hard to please.
Eloise had found at last,
A worm she could adore,
And was busy weaving silken threads
For her bottom drawer.
Alas, he was a common worm,
And Sybil disapproved,
And with such common neighbours,
It was clearly time they moved.
But Eloise was adamant,
She said, 'I love dear Ern,
And though it is a common name,
He's just my kind of worm.
And though he lives up on the common,
Under common ground,
Nothing that you say or do,
Will stop his common round.'

The Spider King

The absent-minded Spider King,
Couldn't quite do anything,
And thro' his web the flies all flew,
For he'd forget to use the glue.
And when he did, he wasn't clever
He'd get his legs all stuck together,
And falling like a bouncing ball
He'd end up sticking to the wall,
And mutter with exasperation,
'Another sticky situation.'
What's the fun of being King,
When you can't do anything?

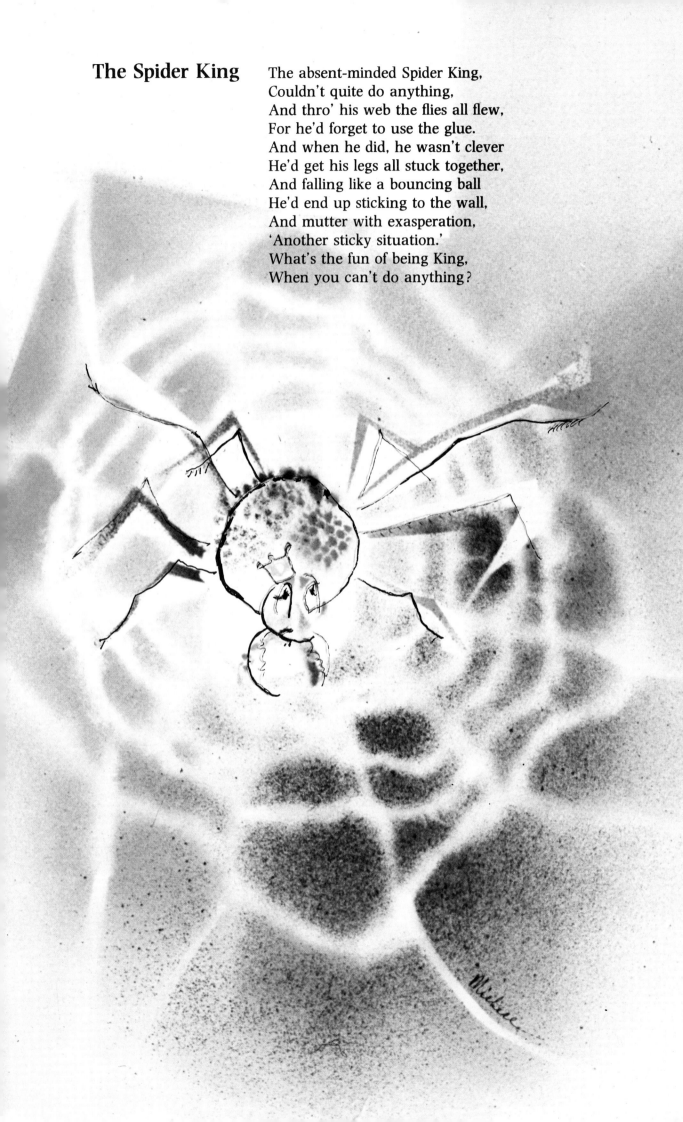

Claude the Crab

Claude an anxious looking crab,
Whose eyes stood out on stalks,
Would stroll about beneath the sea,
On long and lonely walks.
He often tried to reach the beach
Where other crabs reside.
But just when it was in his reach
He'd be swept back by the tide.
Then with six legs he'd scratch his head
And sigh, 'Oh dearie me.
I'm fed up with my deep sea bed,
I'd love to leave the sea.'
And so the weeks and months went by
For poor old anxious Claude,
Without a glimpse of sun or sky.
My word he did get bored.
Until one day a fishing boat
Cast anchor overhead
And dropped a tasty bit of bait
Which fell to the sea bed.
And as it was his breakfast time
And hung within his reach
He tugged and went up with the line
As they headed for the beach.
And Claude who'd never been ashore
Yelled, 'Hang on, wait for me.'
And so they did, and what is more,
They took him home for tea.

Michele

Dilys the Dachshund

Dilys the dachshund hated snow,
Because her middle was so low.
And once when it was really snowing
She only had her tail showing.
So in her woolly winter clothes
She practised walking on her toes,
And with an anxious little grin
Went for a stroll, with stomach in,
And in the middle of her walk
Was spotted by a talent hawk,

Dilys The Dachshund

And in the middle of her walk.
was spotted by a talent hawk.

Who cried, as soon as he had seen her,
He knew she'd make a ballerina.
He'd christen her Dilys Barkover
One day she'd dance with Rudi Rover.
Dilys thrilled at thoughts of fame
Could hardly wait to change her name,
And quickly had the contract signed
Before the hawk could change his mind.
She rushed back home to break the news
And bought some tiny ballet shoes.

She went to London on the train,
In search of fortune and acclaim,
And after weeks of leaps and bounds
And back legs stretch with taller hounds,
Dilys got a lucky break
To play a cygnet in Swan Lake.

She danced so well, with grace and speed,
Some said, she should have got the lead.
And when she did a paw de deux
Everyone applauded her.
'Til Dilys, heady with success
Performed impromptu arabesques
Underneath the royal box,
Where sat the Prince, a handsome fox.
Then jumping up on pointed toes
She spun away across the snow.
The Prince leapt forward with surprise
And raised some glasses to his eyes,
For Dilys, spinning like a top
Had spun so far she couldn't stop.

Musicians paused and frowned uncertain,
Stage hounds whispered 'drop the curtain',
But wait, the Prince stood up and clapped
And then, her shoe elastic snapped.
Disaster!
As high up in the air there flew
A tiny, silken ballet shoe.
Up towards the royal box,
Where stood the Prince, the handsome fox,
He caught it in mid air,
Still warm,
Kissed it,
And a star was born.

And so dear dachshunds be of cheer,
It may well snow for you next year.

The Flea

Jock a Scottish Circus flea,
Could jump a height of one foot three.
And in his kilt, both short and brief
Could bend a mouse hair in his teeth.
He used to get his best applause
As in his silver spangled drawers
And rubber shoes, lest he should slip,
He'd lift a great big orange pip.
Alas, ambition drove too hard
He tried to lift a playing card.
And with assistance from a friend
He got it to stand up on end.

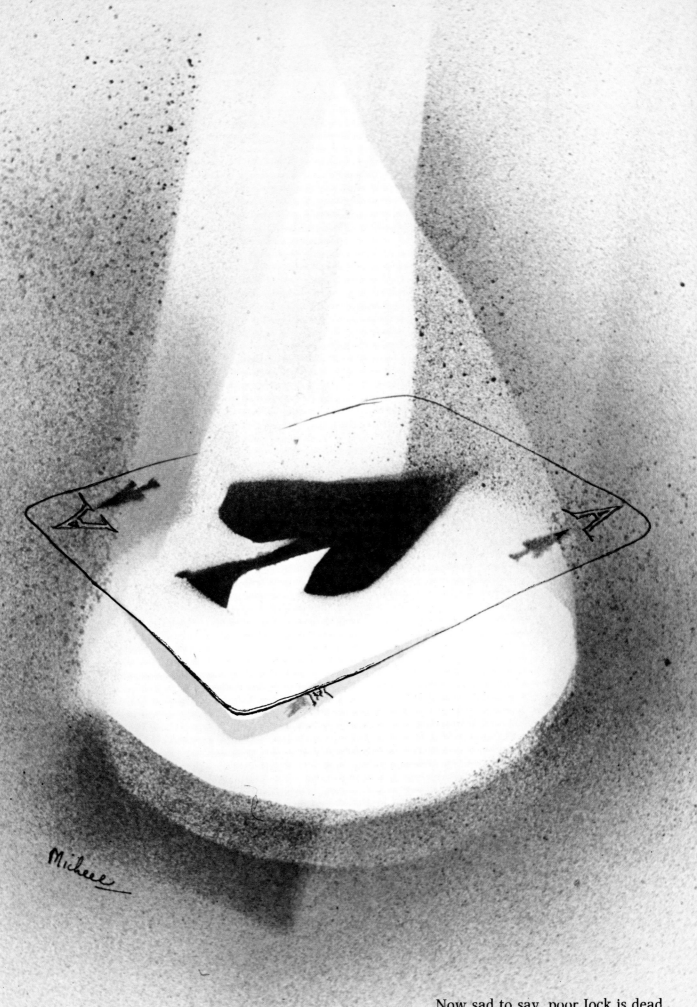

Now sad to say, poor Jock is dead.
The ace of spades fell on his head.
That fatal card!

Dead Matches

Seven dead matches on the floor
And in an ashtray are two more,
And on the scene young P.C. Swan,
Red haired and anxious to get on,
A match for any sort of crime,
But on this case had little time.
The two detectives on their way,
Detective-sergeants, Bryant and May,
Had a flair for finding clues
And there was little time to lose.
So P.C. Swan with puzzled frown
Searched to find who'd struck them down,
And taking off his helmet said,
'Who done this,' and scratched his head.
A fatal move, as it transpired,
Young P.C. Swan at once expired.
And no one yet has solved the crime,
Bryant and May might, given time,
Of seven dead matches on the floor
And in an ashtray are three more.

George the Giraffe

Young George the giraffe
Used to wear a big scarf
And in winter time donned a warm coat.
For he lived in a zoo
And had twice caught the flu,
And often he had a sore throat.
So far from his home
He'd stand there alone
And dream of the African plain,
Where he'd lived as a lad
With his mum and his dad
And he wished he could see them again.
For life in a zoo
When you're prone to the flu
And you've got the world's longest sore throat,
Despite thick pyjamas
And lots of bananas,
Makes you want to get on the next boat.
So next time you go to the zoo
And they show
Every animal there except one,
A lonely giraffe, in a coat and a scarf,
It means George has escaped to the sun.

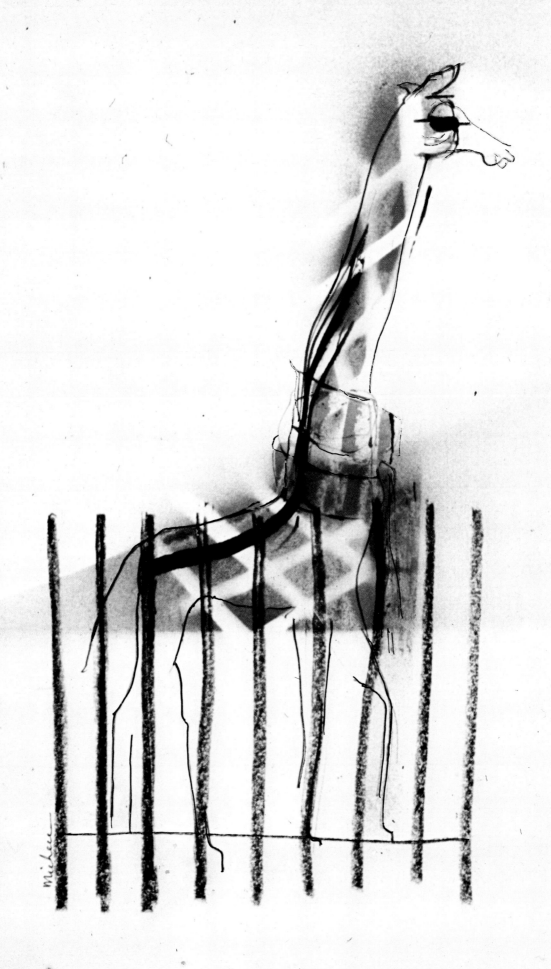

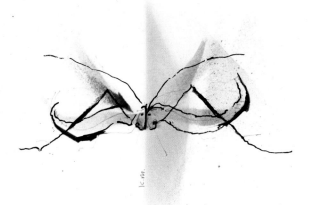

The Grasshopper

A young grasshopper
Whose name was Fred,
Was told by his mother
To go to bed.
But the night was hot,
He couldn't sleep,
So out of the window, with a leap
To jump about and stretch his knees
Till catching cold, he gave a sneeze.
Leaping back he banged his nut,
His sneeze had blown the window shut!

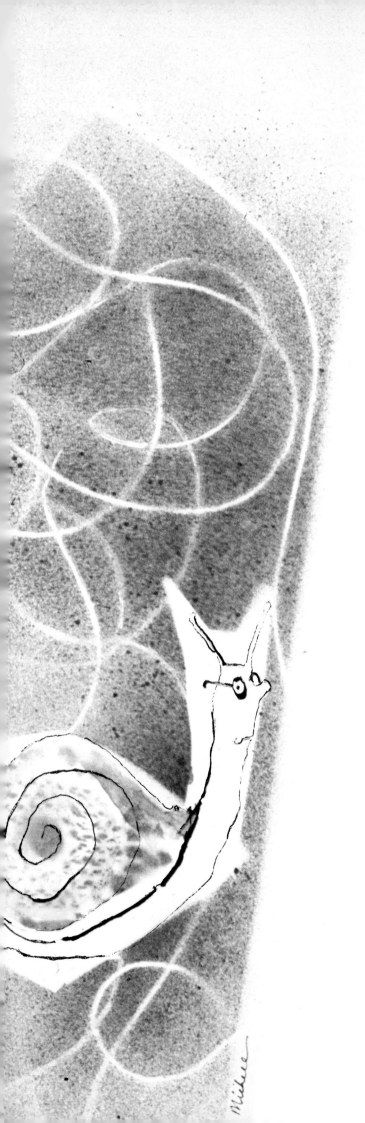

The Snail

Search round in the garden,
You're bound to find a snail.
Perhaps you've always wondered why
They leave a sticky trail?
Some people think it's left for friends
To show which way they're going.
Well, that's not the reason that
A snail leaves a trail showing.
The answer's plain. They cannot see
An inch beyond their noses,
Or recognize the rockery
From a bed of roses.
And snails have no memory
Which gets them in a mess.
That's why they wear their houses,
To remember their address.
And so they leave a sticky trail,
Strange as it may seem.
Not to show the way they've gone,
It's to remind them where they've been.

Harold the Frog

Harold a rather lonely frog,
With spotted, manly chest,
Lived in a wet and squelchy bog
And always looked depressed.
He couldn't get a froggy date,
Although he'd try each night
But when he'd squelch behind a girl
She'd just leap off in fright.
A wallflower at the local hop
He'd dance 'til dawn alone,
Quick, quick, quick, slow, quick
Plop, plop, plop.
Then squelch his way back home.
Reflecting in his private pool
On his unhappy fate,
He wondered why on earth it was
He couldn't get a date
His friends all knew the reason why,
But friends don't like to tell
A frog who's got and doesn't know;
A wet and boggy smell!

Herbert the Hedgehog

Young Herbert the hedgehog
Lived on a hill and his home
Had a wonderful view
Of swans in a lake
Who loved eating cake
That picnickers quite often threw.
And on hot summer days
Young Herbert would gaze
At the children down there having fun,
For he loved watching kites
And some flew to great heights
And often he wished he had one.

And when the days ended
And people packed up all their baskets
To wend their way home,
Young Herbert would sigh and wave them good-bye
For it's not much fun living alone.

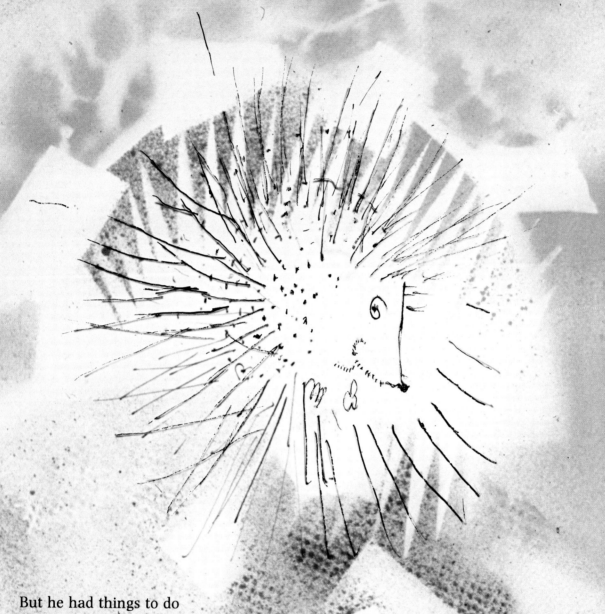

But he had things to do
For spoiling the view
Was the litter, left by one and all.
So Herbert would climb
To the top of his hill and curl himself up in a ball,
Then down he would rush
Like a little brown brush
And the paper would stick on his spikes.
Then he'd dig with his feet
A hole to be neat
For it's litter a hedgehog dislikes.
So next time you picnic
Perhaps by a lake
And you think there's a wonderful view,
Remember a hedgehog who worked very hard
To tidy the place up for you.

The Ginger Cat

A graveyard on a summer's night,
The spectres dance in sheer delight,
And down a moonbeam slides a ginger cat
In plimsolls and a paper hat.

'I'm dead,' he cried, 'My name was Ben,
I had nine lives and just spent ten,
And now I am a ghostly cat,
In plimsolls and a paper hat.'

'Tell us Ben,' the spectres cried,
'The different ways in which you died.'
'Gather round me then,' said Ben,
'And I'll tell you where, and when.'

'The first time I fell down the well,
No one near to hear me yell.'
'How did you escape,' they said,
'When you'd been given up for dead?'

Ginger Cat.

Michele

'I found a bucket,' said the cat,
'And so I went to sleep in that.
And then a local farmer's daughter
Pulled it up to get some water.
Lucky to escape from that,
In plimsolls and a paper hat.'

'The second time, still very clear,
I found a fish head on the pier,
And took it in my mouth with glee,
Then someone threw it in the sea.
They were using it as bait,
I really thought I'd met my fate.'
'How did you escape,' they said,
'When you'd been given up for dead?'

'I met a catfish in the sea,
Who rather liked the look of me,
And pulled me by my ginger tail
To the shore, all cold and pale.
Lucky to escape from that,
In plimsolls and a paper hat.'

'The third time nearly was my end,
Upon a roof top with a friend
I slipped right down a chimney pot
And down towards my doom, I shot.'
'How did you escape,' they said,
'When you'd been given up for dead?'

'But for the soot, I would have died.
They had a chimney sweep inside
And as his brush swept up the flue
Back I popped as good as new.
Lucky to escape from dat!
In plimsolls and a paper hat.'

'The fourth time, in a castle cellar
I met a rat, enormous fellah.
Each eye redder than a ruby
Was I frightened? Wouldn't you be?'
'How did you escape,' they said,
'When you'd been given up for dead?'

'I hid behind a wooden log,
And howled and barked just like a dog.
Oh my, you should have seen him run
I chased him half a mile for fun.
He never knew I was a cat
In plimsolls and a paper hat.'

'The fifth time, on an evening stroll,
I came across a rabbit hole.
And being curious, popped inside
And sitting there a fox I spied.'
'How did you escape,' they said,
'When you'd been given up for dead?'

'I said, dear Fox I've just come here,
To warn you that the hunt is near.'
'Thank you Cat,' the fox replied,
'But for you, I might have died.
I have a friend, for life, a cat
In plimsolls and a paper hat.'

'The sixth time was on Beachy Head,
Sleeping on a disused bed.
When I awoke, I went quite stiff
For it was falling o'er the cliff.'
'How did you escape,' they said,
'When you'd been given up for dead?'

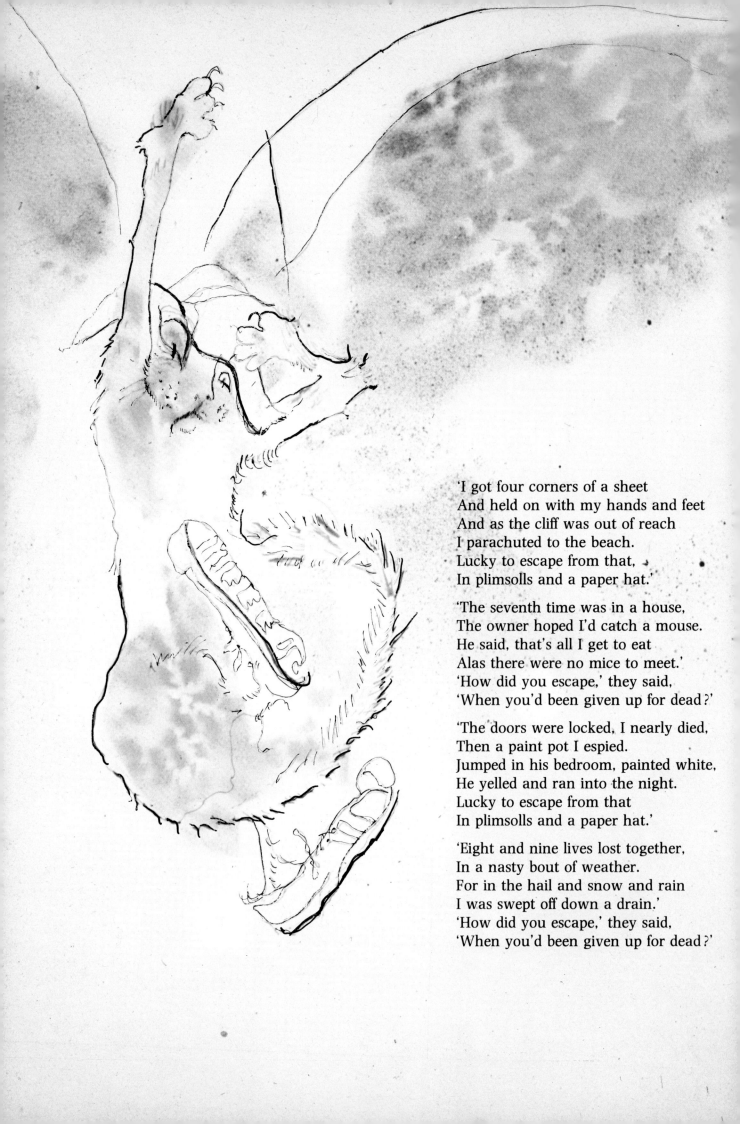

'I got four corners of a sheet
And held on with my hands and feet
And as the cliff was out of reach
I parachuted to the beach.
Lucky to escape from that,
In plimsolls and a paper hat.'

'The seventh time was in a house,
The owner hoped I'd catch a mouse.
He said, that's all I get to eat
Alas there were no mice to meet.'
'How did you escape,' they said,
'When you'd been given up for dead?'

'The doors were locked, I nearly died,
Then a paint pot I espied.
Jumped in his bedroom, painted white,
He yelled and ran into the night.
Lucky to escape from that
In plimsolls and a paper hat.'

'Eight and nine lives lost together,
In a nasty bout of weather.
For in the hail and snow and rain
I was swept off down a drain.'
'How did you escape,' they said,
'When you'd been given up for dead?'

'Lost down below a London street,
A great big turtle did I meet.
Been in the drains since he was small
And knew his way around them all.
Lucky to escape from that,
In plimsolls and a paper hat.'

'And now we come to number ten,
Which really was the end of Ben.
I caught the Cat Flu, how, don't ask it,
And died whilst sleeping in my basket.'

'Now all my lives have gone,' he said,
'Alas, at last I'm really dead.'
Then up the moonbeam climbed the cat
In plimsolls and a paper hat.

Ronald the Rat

Ronald Rat looks quite a swell
And lives in London docks,
He wears a battered bowler hat,
And knee-length yellow socks.
And once he wore a driving glove,
Just to wave to friends,
But alas, he has no car,
For Ronald just pretends.
He's not a millionaire at all,
Just a dockside rat,
But you'd never guess,
When he wears his glove,
And socks and bowler hat.

Wilfred the Weasel

The church bell strikes
The hour of noon,
In the village on the hill,
And across the fields and meadows,
Echoes its thin silver note,
To the ears of Wilfred Weasel,
Seated at his artist's easel,
As he waits for inspiration,
In his floppy hat and coat,
Brush in hand and palette ready,
As he's been since half past eight,
Empty canvas indicating
Inspiration's sleeping late.
But though the bell notes fade forever,
Conjured up and left behind,
In a blinding flash
A vision clear as crystal in his mind.

With all the style of Leonardo
And daring use of green and blue
Deft strokes tell a moving story,
'Gone to lunch and back at two.'

Peg the Baby Hen

A baby hen, whose name was Peg,
Said, 'Mummy, can I lay an egg?
I wish you'd show me what to do,
Then I could help you with a few.'
Her mother smiled, and shook her head.
'You're far too young for that,' she said,

'But do the things that you've been taught,
And think a nice round eggy thought
And one day, it will come to pass,
An egg will pop out on the grass.'

Thelma the Thrush

Thelma the thrush
Made her home in a train.
Just under the engine
To keep out the rain.
Along came the driver
Who said, 'Oh my word.
I can't move the train
Or I'll frighten the bird.'
Along came the head
Of the railway track,
Who said to the driver,
'I'll give you the sack.
Drive off at once,
You're already late.'
'Not me,' said the driver,
'Nor me,' said his mate,
And smiled down at Thelma
Who looked quite dismayed,
For while they'd been talking
Four eggs had been laid.

'Well that's it.' said the
Head of the railway track.
'You can't drive off now
Or the eggs will all crack.
I'd best phone the station,
But what shall I say?'
Said the driver, 'The truth,
Uneggspected delay.'

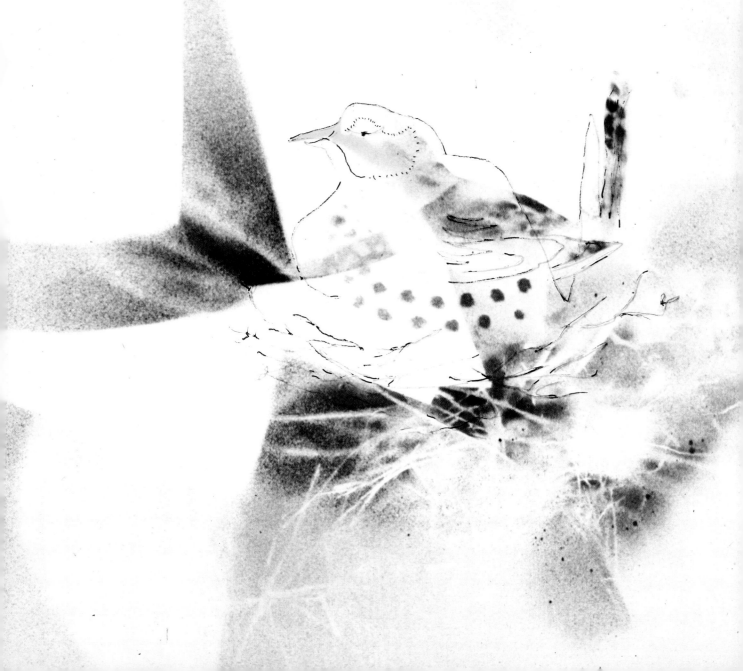

Norman the Zebra

Norman, a zebra at the zoo,
Escaped and ran to Waterloo
And caused a lot of consternation,
In the rush-hour, at the station.
He had an awful lot of fun
Chasing folk on Platform 1,

And then he ran to Regent's Park
And hid there until it was dark,
And thought of his keeper Mr Prout,
How cross he'd be, that he'd got out.
So he tiptoed to the big zoo gate
And found he'd got there just too late.
Poor Norman had a little weep
And lay down in the road to sleep
And woke up early from his rest,
With people walking on his chest.
And someone said, 'I think that's new,
A zebra crossing near the zoo.'
And with a snort of indignation,
Regretting leaving for the station,
He cried, 'I've had enough of that,
How dare you use me as a mat.
I'm going straight home to the zoo.'
He was just in time for breakfast too.

A Penniless French Mouse

A penniless French mouse called Jacques,
In beret, boots and belted mac,
Strode idly down an empty drain
Protected 'gainst the wind and rain,
When from a grating in the street
A cigarette fell at his feet,
And in surprise, he cried:
'Mon Dieu!
It is my favourite brand,
Disque Bleu.
Ma foi, these are très fort,' he said.
Inhaling deep, the end glowed red.
A smell, he thought, was just le drain,
Was gas escaping from le main.
Le grande explosion, au r'voir Jacques,
In beret, boots and belted mac.

And now he has gone
To the great mousehole in the sky,
Where mountains of le cheese
Stretch away as far as the eye can see.
'Excusez-moi, monsieur . . .'
'Oui?'
'Which way to le roquefort s'il vous plaît?'

NATHANIAL GNAT

The Gnat

The statue is tiny
I doubt that you'd see it
But it's no less important for that:
It's an insect resplendent
In top hat and tails
And inscribed to 'Nathaniel Gnat'.
Look at his tile
Ain't it got style
Butchers the weasel and stoat,
That's cockney for hat and his coat
And all that,
Which accounts for the smile on his boat.
He departed this world
Umbrella well furled
When his spats tangled up with some trees.
A strange way to die
For a gnat who could tie
A cravat with such elegant ease.
Some witnesses said
Though he fell on his head
He could have been saved by his hat,
But smart to the last
Although falling fast
He removed it in case it went flat.
Now thanks to his style
And that brave marble smile
We find, when with clothes we're impressed,
That we tend to apply,
And now you know why,
The expression 'He's nattily dressed'.

My Best Friend

Save for the humming of the bees
And raindrops falling thro' the trees,
The wood was silent as a grave
Whilst shafts of sunlight made a brave
Attempt to pierce the velvet gloom
As lonely as an empty room.
Alone was I, but not afraid,
The friend I'd been with must have strayed,
For tho' I called, no answer came
And so I played a splendid game
In the bracken wet and thick
With my favourite walking stick.
And then, a voice called out quite near:
'So there you are, old chap, come here.'
And sitting there, upon a log
Was my best friend, who said: 'Good dog.'

The Haggis Season

The haggis season has begun.
All over Scotland every gun
Is taken down with loving care,
Though some prefer the haggis snare
For haggis are a wily lot,
That's why they are so seldom shot.
Then hidden in the Highland heather
Great hairy clansmen crouch together,
And having laid the haggis bait
(A lifelike haggis on a plate),
One cries out loudly 'There the noo!'
Which means a haggis is in view.
It's flying upside down and low
The guns all fire but they're too slow.
For though it's rather old and fat
They're awful hard to hit like that!
And as it flies off in the mists,
Great hairy clansmen shake their fists
And scream their curses to the crags
Then stamp on empty haggis bags.
And so the haggis gets away to live
Until next Hogmanay.
And that's the reason it's so rare,
This strange traditional Scottish fare.

Roman Salki

Jeremy Lloyd

Is well known as an actor, both here
and in the United States. He has
contributed to, and appeared in, *Rowan
and Martin's Laugh In*, and while acting,
contributed to many other TV shows.
Now he has given up acting and is
concentrating solely on his writing.
He is the co-author of the very
successful TV series *Are You Being
Served?*, and, with Lance Percival, writes
the *Whodunnit* programme. He also
writes lyrics, and is the author of a
novel, *Further Adventures of Captain
Gregory Dangerfield*, which has been
published here and in the United
States.

Bruce Atkins

Keith Michell

Artistic Director of the Chichester
Festival Theatre, Keith Michell has
starred in many plays, in London and
on Broadway. He has acted at Stratford
and the Old Vic; has starred in musicals,
including *Irma La Douce*, and *Robert and
Elizabeth*; and has appeared in films and
on television. He is perhaps best known
for his role as Henry VIII in the
television series *The Six Wives of
Henry VIII*. He has made recordings,
and has held several exhibitions of his
paintings. This year at Chichester he
combined his talents, directing and
designing *Twelfth Night*. Keith Michell
was born in Australia, is married and
has a son and a daughter.